It's Easy To Play West End Hits.

Wise Publications
London / New York / Paris / Sydney

Exclusive Distributors:
Music Sales Limited
8/9 Frith Street, London W1V 5TZ, England.
Music Sales Pty Limited
120 Rothschild Avenue, Rosebery, NSW 2018, Australia.

This book © Copyright 1993 by
Wise Publications
Order No.AM90097
ISBN 0-7119-3168-2

Book design by Michael Bell Design
Cover illustration by Gillian Martin
Compiled by Peter Evans
Music arranged by Frank Booth

Music Sales' complete catalogue lists thousands of titles and
is free from your local music shop or direct from Music Sales Limited.
Please send a cheque/postal order for £1.50 for postage to:
Music Sales Limited, Newmarket Road, Bury St. Edmunds, Suffolk IP33 3YB.

Printed in the United Kingdom by
Caligraving Limited, Thetford, Norfolk.

A Fine Romance

from Swing Time

Music by Jerome Kern.
Words by Dorothy Fields.

All I Ask Of You

from The Phantom Of The Opera

Music by Andrew Lloyd Webber.
Lyrics by Charles Hart. Additional Lyrics by Richard Stilgoe.

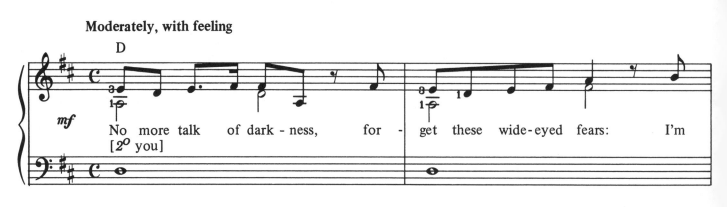

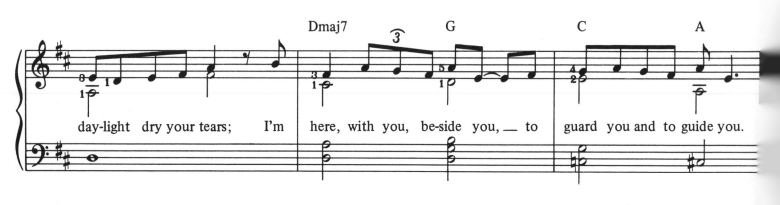

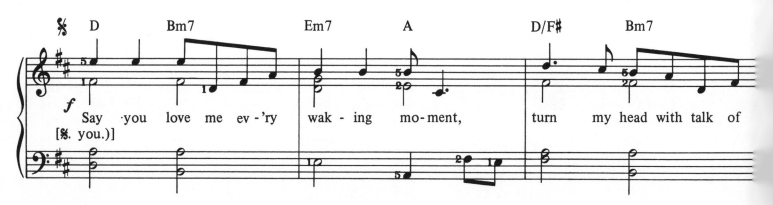

VERSE 2:
Let me be your shelter, let me be your light;
You're safe, no one will find you,
Your fears are far behind you.
All I want is freedom, a world with no more night;
And you always beside me, to hold me and to hide me.

Then say you'll share with me one love, one lifetime
Let me lead you from your solitude.
Say you need me with you, here beside you,
Anywhere you go, let me go too;
Christine, that's all I ask of you.

D.S.
Say you'll share with me one love, one lifetime;
Say the word and I will follow you.
Share each day with me, each night, each morning.
Say you love me! You know I do.
Love me, that's all I ask of you.

Five Guys Named Moe

Words & Music by Larry Wynn & Jerry Bresler.

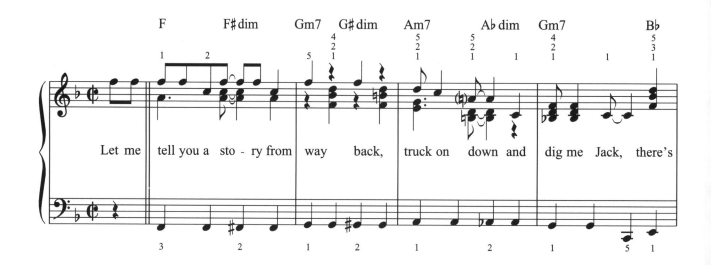

Let me tell you a sto - ry from way back, truck on down and dig me Jack, there's

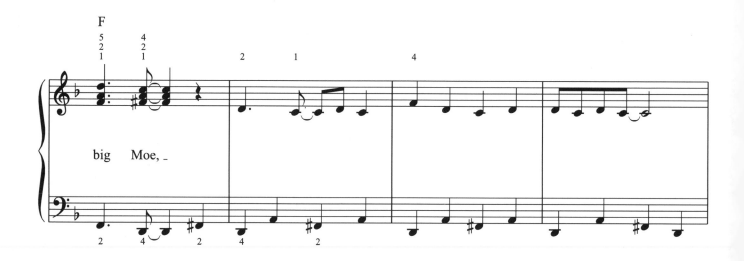

big Moe, —

lit - tle bid - dy Moe,

9

Moe, Ah! | We came out from no - where, | that don't mean a | thing.

We rate high __ | and you'll know why __ | when you hear us | sing, _____

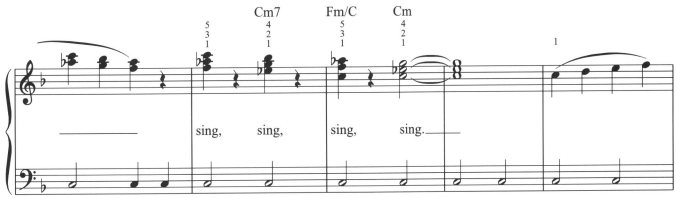

_____ | sing, sing, | sing, sing. _____ |

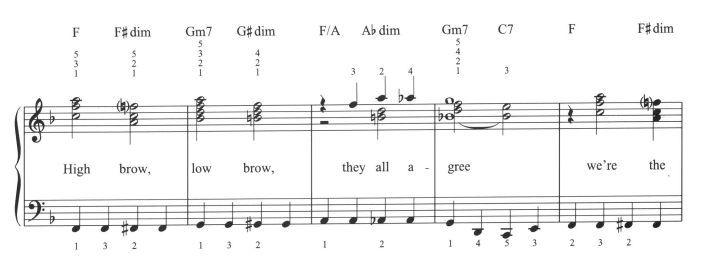

High brow, | low brow, | they all a - gree | we're the

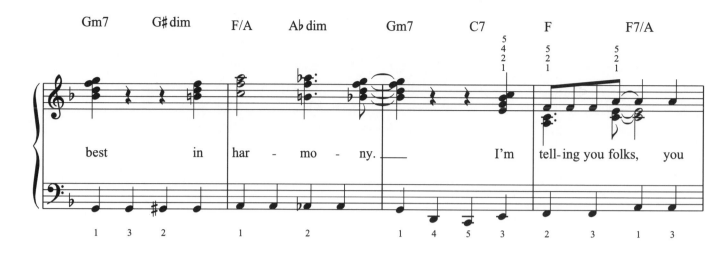

best   in   har - mo - ny.   I'm   tell-ing you folks,   you

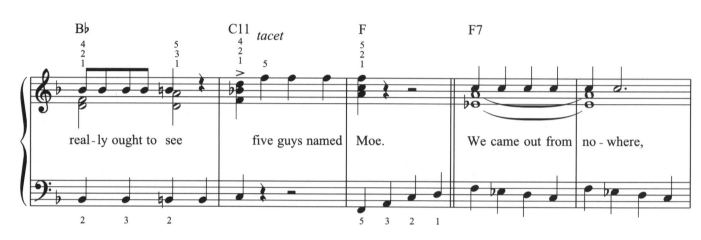

real-ly ought to see   five guys named Moe.   We came out from no - where,

that don't mean a   thing.   We rate high _ and you'll know why _

when you hear us   sing, _____

I Know Him So Well

from Chess

Words & Music by Benny Andersson, Tim Rice & Bjorn Ulvaeus.

Fairly slowly

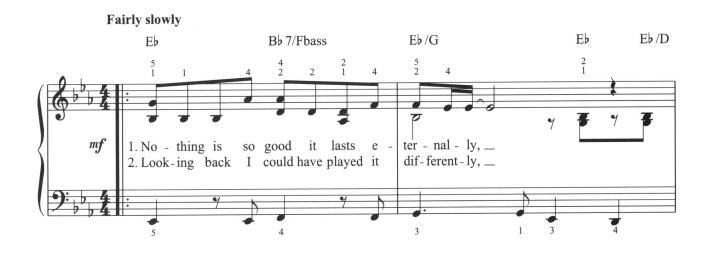

1. No - thing is so good it lasts e - ter - nal - ly, __
2. Look - ing back I could have played it dif - ferent - ly, __

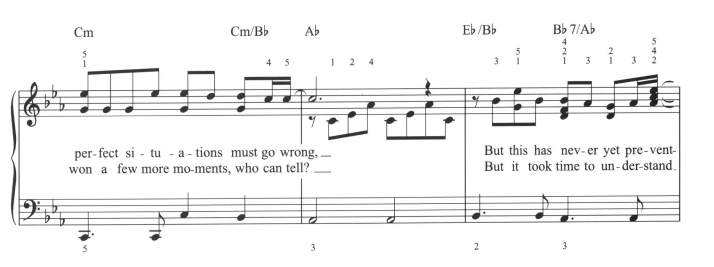

per - fect si - tu - a - tions must go wrong, __
won a few more mo - ments, who can tell? __

But this has nev - er yet pre - vent-
But it took time to un - der - stand.

- ed me __
_____ the man. __

want - ing far too much for far too
Now at least I know I know him

3. No one in your life is with you constantly,
   No one is completely on your side.
   And though I move my world to be with him,
   Still the gap between us is too wide.

4. Looking back I could have played it differently,
   Learned about the man before I fell.
   But I was ever so much younger then,
   Now at least I know him well.

   Wasn't it good? *etc.*

I Dreamed A Dream

from Les Misérables

Music by Claude-Michel Schönberg. Lyric by Herbert Kretzmer.
Original text by Alain Boublil & Jean-Marc Natel.

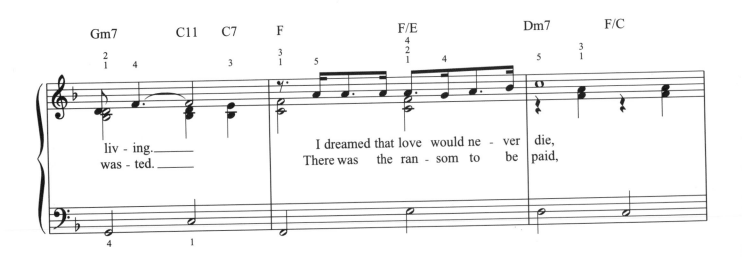

Is You Is, Or Is You Ain't (Ma' Baby)

from Five Guys Named Moe

Words & Music by Billy Austin & Louis Jordan.

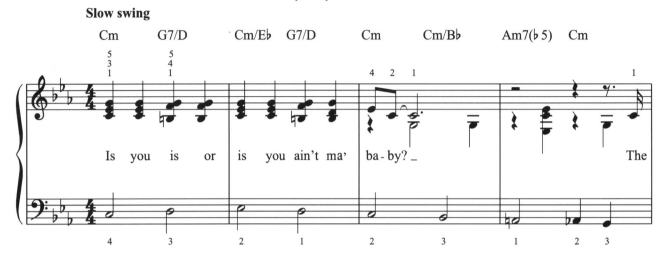

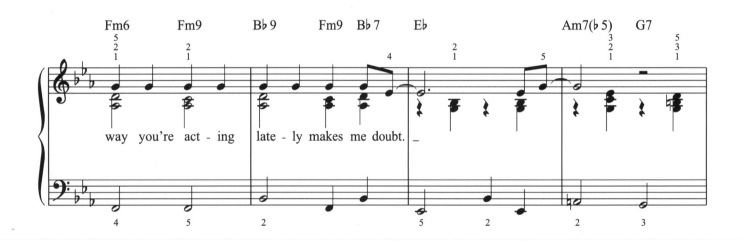

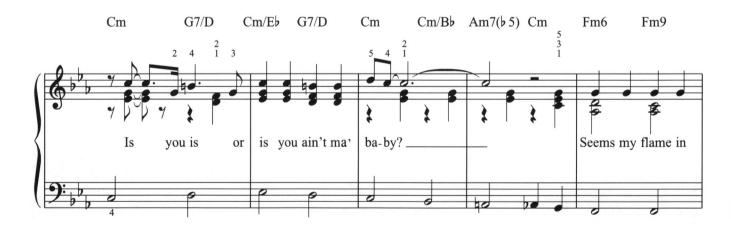

your heart's done gone out. My friends say I could do a lot bet-

-ter,___ if this keeps up I'll soon need a nurse.___ I know I can't do a-ny

bet-ter, ___ but be-lieve me, I could do a lot worse._____ Is you is or

is you ain't ma' ba-by? _____ The way you're act-ing

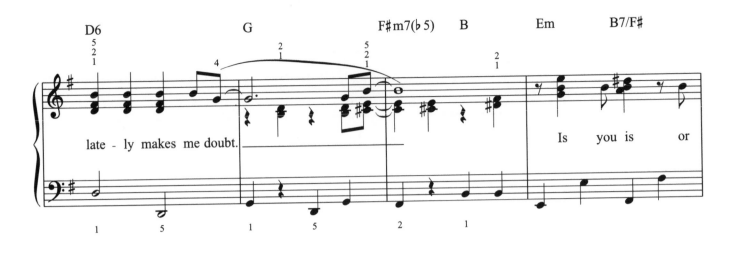

late - ly makes me doubt. _____ Is you is or

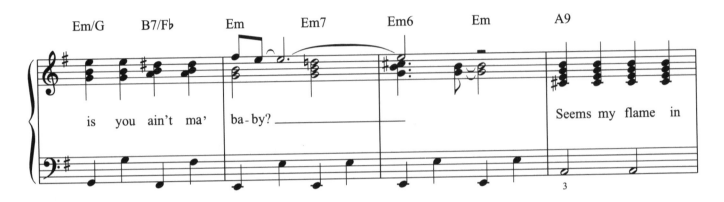

is you ain't ma' ba - by? _____ Seems my flame in

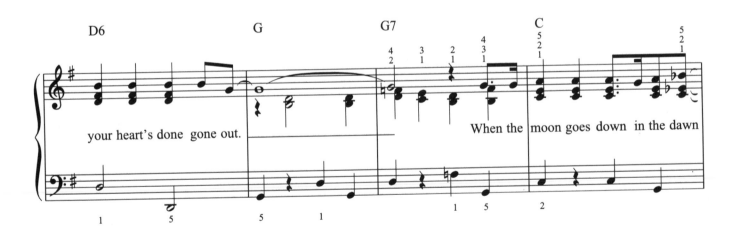

your heart's done gone out. When the moon goes down in the dawn

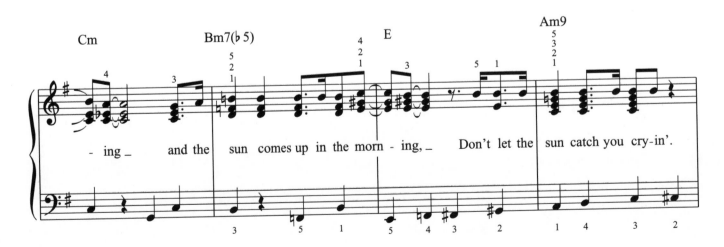

- ing _ and the sun comes up in the morn - ing, _ Don't let the sun catch you cry-in'.

When the moon goes down in the dawn - ing,___ don't let the sun catch you cry-in' if your

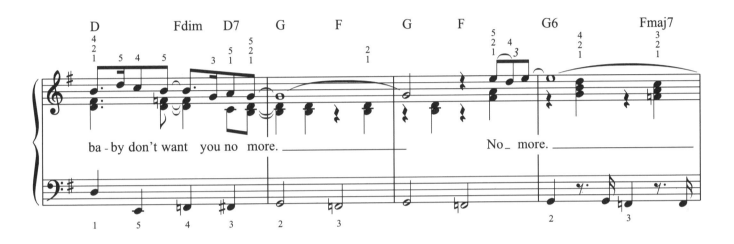

ba - by don't want you no more. ___ No___ more. ___

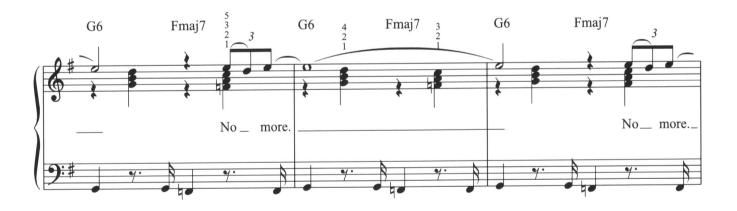

___ No ___ more. ___ No ___ more. ___

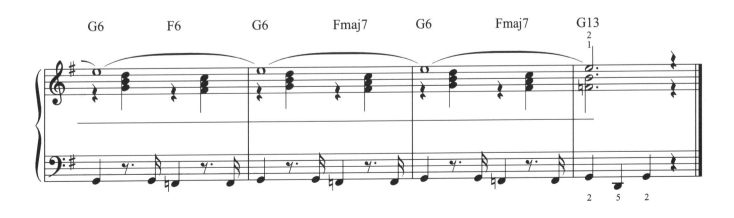

Tell Me It's Not True

from Blood Brothers

Words & Music by Willy Russell.

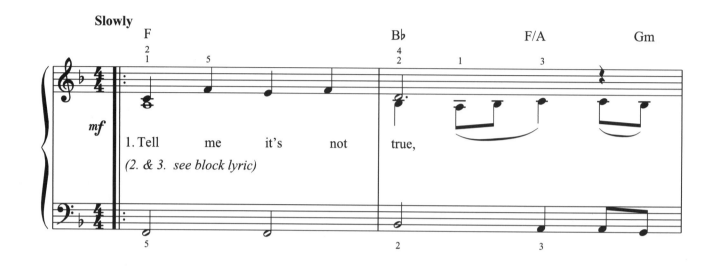

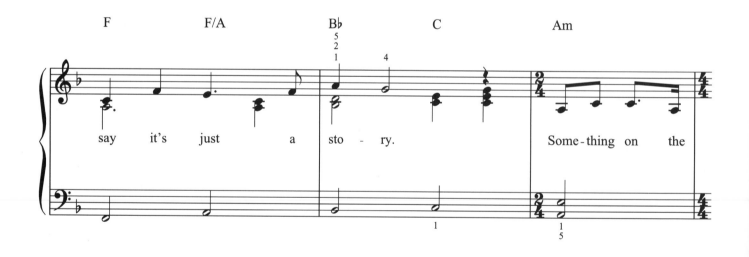

Though it's here be - fore me, say it's just a dream,

say it's just a scene _____ from an old mo - vie of years _____ a -

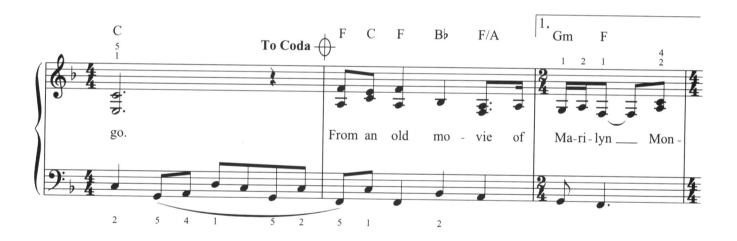

go. From an old mo - vie of Ma - ri - lyn _____ Mon -

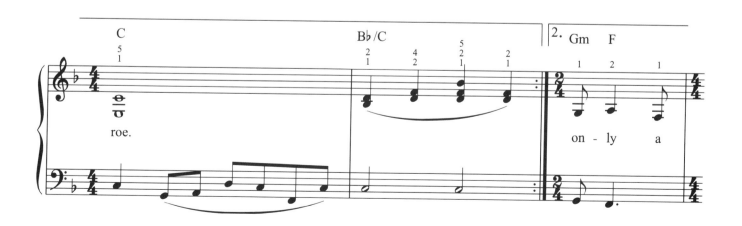

roe. on - ly a

2. Say it's just some clowns,
   Two players in the lime-light,
   Bring the curtain down.
   Say it's just two clowns,
   Who couldn't get their lines right,
   Say it's just a show on the radio
   That we can turn over and start again,
   That we can turn over, it's only a game.

3. Tell me it's not true,
   Say I only dreamed it and morning will come soon.
   Tell me it's not true,
   Say you didn't mean it,
   Say it's just pretend,
   Say it's just the end of an old
   Movie from years ago.
   From an old movie with Marilyn Monroe.

   Tell me it's not true, say you didn't mean it.
   Say it's just pretend, say it's just the end of an old movie from years ago.
   Of an old movie with Marilyn Monroe.

The American Dream

from Miss Saigon

Music by Claude-Michel Schönberg. Lyrics by Richard Maltby Jr. & Alain Boublil.
Adapted from the original French Lyrics by Alain Boublil

Bums there have mo - ney to spare, ___ the A - mer - i - can dream. ___
Wall Street is rea - dy to sell, ___

Cars that have bars take you there, ___ the A - mer - i - can dream. ___
Come, make a life from thin air, ___

On stage each night Fred As - taire, ___
Come and get more than your share, ___

___ the A - mer - i - can dream. ___

Schlitz down the drain, ___ pop the cham - pagne,

The Time Warp

from The Rocky Horror Show

Words & Music by Richard O'Brien.

Medium rock beat

It's a - stound - ing, __ time __ is flee - ing;

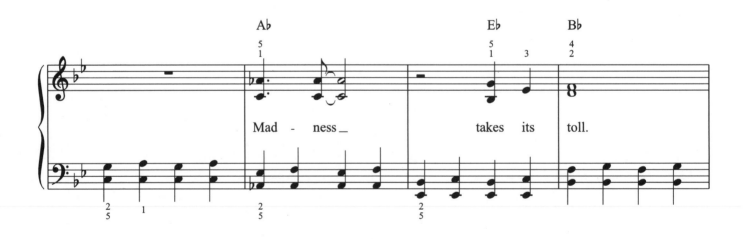

Mad - ness __ takes its toll.

But lis - ten close - - ly, __ not for ver - y much long-

- - er; ____ I've got __ to

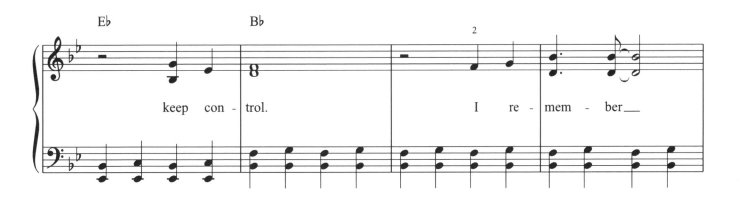

keep con - trol. I re - mem - ber __

do - ing the Time _____ Warp, __

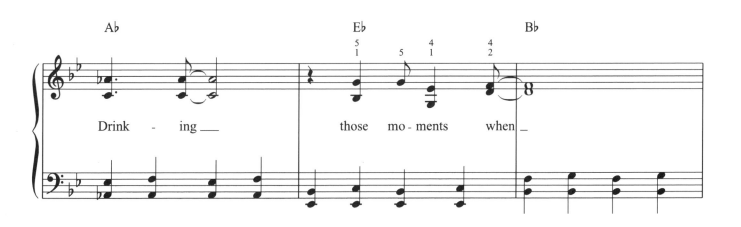

Drink - ing ___ those mo - ments when __

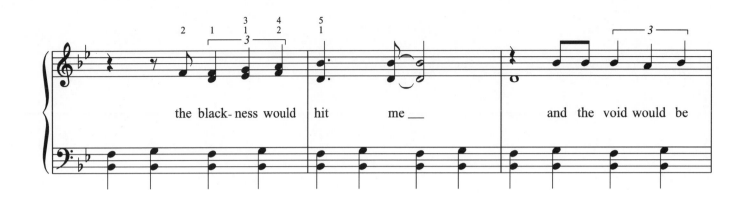

the black-ness would hit me ___ and the void would be

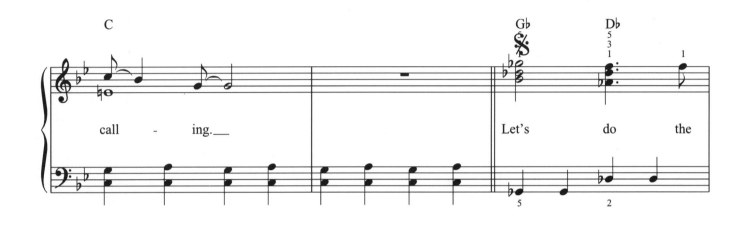

call - ing. ___ Let's do the

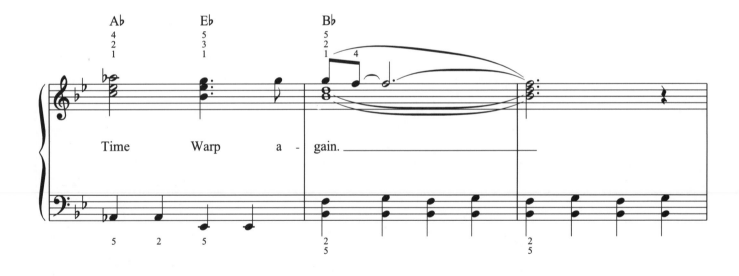

Time Warp a - gain. ___

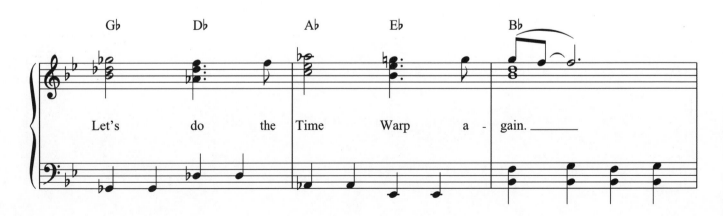

Let's do the Time Warp a - gain. ___

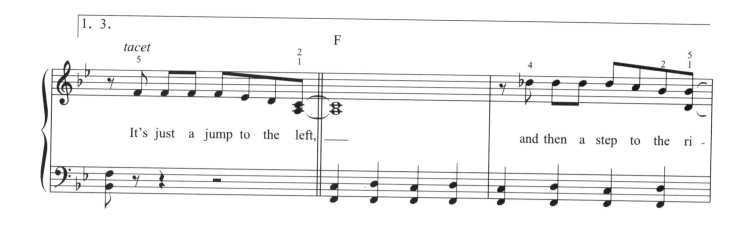

It's just a jump to the left, ___ and then a step to the ri -

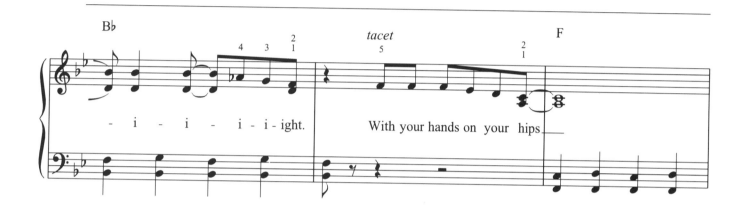

- i - i - i - i - ight. With your hands on your hips ___

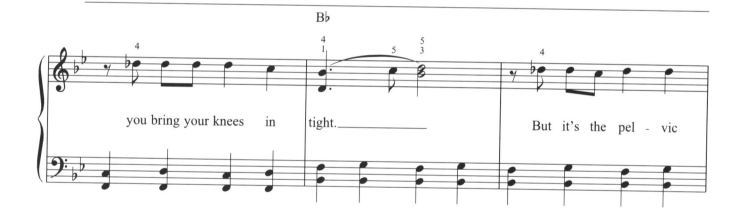

you bring your knees in tight. ___ But it's the pel - vic

thrust ___ that near - ly drives you in - sa - a - a - a - a - ane. ___

snake of a guy_ gave me an e - vil eye.__ We - ll it shook me up, _ it took me

by sur - prise,. He had a pick-up truck_ and the de - vil's __ eyes. __ He

stared at me__ and I felt a change,__ Time meant noth - ing, nev - er

D. %̸ al Coda

CODA

would a - gain.__

gain. _____

2. It's so dreamy, oh fantasy free me, so you can't see me, so you can't see me no, not at all.
In another dimension, with voyeuristic intention, well secluded, I'll see all.
With a bit of a mind-flip, you're into the time-slip,
Nothing can ever be the same, you're spaced out on sensation,
Like you're under sedation. Let's do the Time Warp *etc*.

Well All Right

from Buddy

Words & Music by Jerry Allison, Buddy Holly, Joe Maudlin & Norman Petty.

Moderately, with a strong beat

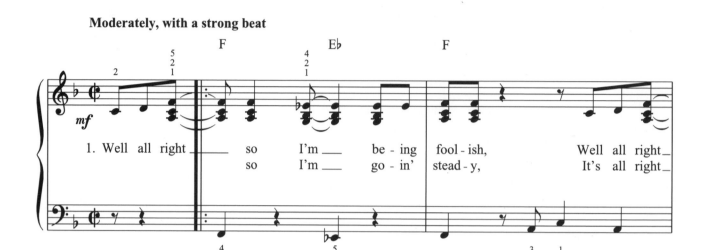

1. Well all right _____ so I'm _____ be - ing fool - ish, Well all right _____
so I'm _____ go - in' stead - y, It's all right _____

_____ let peo - ple know _____ A - bout the dreams and wish - es you _____
_____ when peo - ple say, _____ That those fool - ish kids can't be read -

_____ wish _____ in the night _____ when lights _____ are low. _____ Well all right, _____ Well all right, _____
- y _____ for the love _____ that comes _____ their way. _____

Oh, well ___ live and love with all our might,___ Well all right,___

Well all right, ___ Our ___ life - time love will

1.
be all right.___ 2. Well all right

2.
be all right. ___

The Last Night Of The World

from Miss Saigon

Music by Claude-Michel Schönberg. Lyrics by Richard Maltby Jr. & Alain Boublil.
Adapted from the original French Lyrics by Alain Boublil.

I will sing with you. Our song played on a so-lo sax-o-phone, __ so stay with me __ and hold me tight __ and dance like it's the last night of the world. __

48